PRIMITIVE ART

IN THE COLLECTIONS OF

THE ART INSTITUTE OF CHICAGO

The Art Institute of Chicago

Copyright by The Art Institute of Chicago 1965
Library of Congress Catalog Card Number: 65-18942
Printed in the United States of America by Low's Incorporated
Design by Everett McNear

ABOVE: *Feather Ornament*. Nazca Culture, South Coast Peru, A.D. 1 - 300. Hummingbird feathers, gold, reed. Height 5⅝ in. Collected by Pablo Soldi. Mrs. Chauncey B. Borland Fund 56.402.

It has recently been suggested that these delicate and remarkably well preserved objects were worn as forehead ornaments. (See Sawyer, A., 1961, note 11).

ON THE COVER: *Ceremonial Knife*. Chimu Culture, Lambayeque Valley, North Coast Peru, A.D. 1300 - 1500. Gold, turquoise inlay. Height 13½ in. Ada Turnbull Hertle Fund 63.841.

Such knives were probably made to be carried in ceremonial processions. The figure on the handle is thought to represent Naym-Lap, a legendary hero who colonized the Lambayeque Valley. Reference: Burlington Magazine, p 539, pl. 74.

BACK COVER: *Feather Poncho*. Chimu Culture, provenance unknown, A.D. 1000 - 1300. Plain woven cotton cloth, feathers applied. Height 33¾ in., width 33¼. Buckingham Fund 55.1789.

This poncho, demonstrating a sensitive use of the feather mosaic technique, has a similar design on the back. Ex Coll. Gaffron. References: Bennett, W., fig. 120; Christensen, E., fig. 253; Doering, H.U. 1952, pl. 51; Keleman, P., pl. 290a; Lehmann, W. and Doering, H.U., color plate XII; Leicht, H., pl. 16; Lothrop, S.K., p. 186, ill.

Tripod bowl. Maya Culture, North Guatemala (?) 400-900 A.D. Terra cotta. Diameter 12¾ in. Suzette Morton Zurcher Restricted Fund 64.299. This fine example of Maya painting shows an unusually extensive use of the lavender color.

ANY CATALOGUE dealing with a broad museum collection such as this one reveals, by inference, some of the history of the institution and the particular department with which it is concerned. A glance through this handbook will show a number of strengths and weaknesses which require some explanation in order to give a proper context to the collections of primitive art. It will be noted, for example, that almost all of the objects here illustrated were acquired in 1955 or afterwards. The ancient arts of Peru will be seen to be represented in considerable depth while those objects from Middle and North America, Africa and Melanesia might appear to have been selected in a somewhat more haphazard fashion. A brief review of the history of the department of primitive art will justify some of these apparent shortcomings and serve as a background for what is hoped will be the course of future acquisitions.

Before 1955, and beginning as early as 1889, a number of miscellaneous examples of primitive art drifted into the collections of the Art Institute where they became all but forgotten in various storerooms. Although little of this material was of great importance, some significant gold pieces from Panama and Colombia were given through the Antiquarian Society, a fine Benin plaque fragment was fortuitously purchased in 1933, and Mrs. Gilbert Chapman donated a group of Melanesian objects in 1952. In 1955 an important focus was suddenly given to this disparate group of objects with the purchase of the famed Gaffron collection of Peruvian art. This was due to the efforts of Daniel Catton Rich, then director, and Alan Sawyer, then an associate curator in the Department of Decorative Arts. Coincidentally, the Wassermann collection, another renowned group of Peruvian ceramics, was sold to Nathan Cummings, who generously gave the bulk of it to this museum. In a short time, the Art Institute thus came to have one of the finest collections of Peruvian art in the world.

Recognizing the growth of public interest and the new activity which was being demonstrated by local collectors in the area of primitive art, an advisory committee was formed by James Alsdorf, and in 1957 the youngest fine arts department of the Art Institute came into being under the curatorship of Alan Sawyer. It was felt by both the committee and the curator that the arts of primitive peoples should be included in the collections of the Art Institute, but that only objects of the highest aesthetic quality would be chosen. It was further believed that where possible some of the stylistic and chronological gaps in the Peruvian holdings should be filled when the opportunities existed. This goal was aided by the continuing interest of Mr. Cummings with the gift of some highly significant Paracas ceramics and the donation of a rare vessel from the early Cupisnique culture by Mr. and Mrs. Raymond Wielgus.

Because of the increasing scarcity of good material and the necessarily limited funds available to such a young department, it has also been a recent policy not to seek examples of styles which are already well represented in the collections of the Chicago Natural History Museum. Few objects from Melanesia and Polynesia are therefore to be found in the Art Institute, but considerable activity has been possible in the area of African art and Middle American archaeology.

These remarks may help explain the acquisition policy which has been responsible for this collection. The most important aspect of this brief history, however, is the continuing support to this work which has been given by local collectors and the committee members. Whether the donations have been in the form of important objects themselves or as restricted cash gifts to the acquisition fund, very little could have been accomplished without this interest and encouragement.

To predict the future, then, we must start by assuming that this generosity will continue. Hopefully, this is not a risky prediction, but it is somewhat more difficult to tell what sort of objects we can expect to enter the collections in the near future. We have noted an increasing scarcity of fine pieces from Africa due to the fact that they are no longer being made, and what remains is being avidly bought by other museums and private collectors. It is probable, therefore, that more of our future acquisitions will be in the area of the ancient arts of Middle and South America which are not of such an ephemeral nature, and are available with some regularity. It must finally be realized that these collections will never attain the wealth and depth of those in older and better endowed institutions. If in some small way, however, representation of the great artistic achievements of these exotic cultures can be imparted to those who visit The Art Institute of Chicago, our aims will have been achieved.

ALLEN WARDWELL
Curator, Primitive Art Department

3

4

2

1   *Mummy Mask.* Mochica Culture, North Coast Peru, A.D. 400 - 600. Copper, shell, pyrite, gold and cinnabar. Height 6¾ in. Gift of Mr. and Mrs. Nathan Cummings 57.375.

These masks, made for burial, were probably attached to mummy bundles. Ex Coll. Wassermann. References: Bird, J., p. 207, fig. 56; New York, Cooper Union, No. 26; Sawyer, A. 1954, p. 35, ill.

2   *Mummy Mask.* Mochica Culture, North Coast Peru, A.D. 400 - 600. Copper, shell, pyrite. Height 7⅞ in. Gift of Mr. and Mrs. Nathan Cummings 60.900.

Ex Coll. Wassermann. References: AIC Annual Report 1960 - 1961, p. 16, ill.; Chicago, Art Institute 1960, No. 68, ill.; New York, Cooper Union, No. 27, ill. (See also note for No. 1).

3   *Head Beaker.* Ica Valley, South Coast Peru, A.D. 1300 - 1500. Gold. Height 6⅝ in. Buckingham Fund 55.2587.

Ex Coll. Gaffron. References: AIC Quarterlies, Vol. XLVI, No. 2, p. 28, ill., Vol. L, No. 1, p. 2, ill.; Bennett, W., fig. 100; Dockstader, F., p. 31, ill.; Doering, H.U., 1952, fig. 85; Lehmann, W. and Doering, H.U., fig. 103.

4   *Hummingbird Ear Plugs.* Ica Culture, South Coast Peru, A.D. 1000 - 1470. Gold, garnet inlay. Diameter 1¾ in. Buckingham Fund 55.2594a-b.

Ex Coll. Gaffron. References: AIC Quarterly, Vol. 50, No. 1, p. 6, ill.; Bennett, W., fig. 113; Chicago, Art Institute 1957b, p. 45, ill.; Keleman, P. pl. 209c; Lehmann, W. and Doering, H.U., fig. 106b.

5

6

7

8

5   *Jar*. Paracas Culture, Ocucaje Style, Ica Valley, South Coast Peru, ca. 300 B.C. Terra cotta, resin paint. Height 11⅝ in. Gift of Mr. and Mrs. Nathan Cummings 60.897.

This jar is notable for its large size and unusually fine state. Collected by Pablo Soldi. References: Chicago, Art Institute 1960, No. 55, ill.; Chicago, Arts Club, No. 80, ill.

6   *Stirrup Spout Vessel*. Cupisnique Culture, North Coast Peru, 900 - 500 B.C. Terra cotta. Height 9¼ in. Gift of Mr. and Mrs. Raymond Wielgus 62.698.

Cupisnique vessels, the earliest ceramics from the North Coast, all show the heavy proportions evident here.

7   *Fish Bowl*. Paracas Culture, Ocucaje Style, Ica Valley, South Coast Peru, ca. 100 B.C. Terra cotta. Diameter 7½ in. Gift of Mr. and Mrs. Nathan Cummings 60.898.

This bowl is a pair to one in the collection of The Metropolitan Museum of Art. Collected by Pablo Soldi. References: Chicago, Art Institute 1960, No. 55e; Sawyer, A. 1961, p. 297, fig. 12a (drawing).

8   *Double Spout Feline Bottle*. Paracas Culture, Ocucaje Style, Ica Valley, South Coast Peru, ca. 600 B.C. Terra cotta, resin paint. Height 6⅜ in. Gift of Mr. and Mrs. Nathan Cummings 60.895.

A fine example of the Ocucaje resin painting decoration. The bottle was found with a body wrapped in white cotton cloth. Collected by Pablo Soldi. References: Chicago, Art Institute 1960, No. 55f, ill.; Sawyer, A. 1961, p. 284, fig. 6i (drawing).

9

10

11

12

9 *Quail Effigy Beaker.* Nazca Culture, South Coast Peru, A.D. 300 - 500. Terra cotta. Height 8⅛ in. Buckingham Fund 55.1965.

Ex Coll. Gaffron. References: Bennett, W., fig. 65; Chicago, Art Institute 1957b, p. 43, ill.; Christensen, E., pl. 240.

10 *Fish Jar.* Nazca Culture, Ingenio Valley, South Coast Peru, A.D. 1 - 300. Terra cotta. Height 6¾ in. E. E. Ayer Fund and S. B. Williams Fund 56.1151.

11 *Fish Demon Double Spout Vessel.* Nazca Culture, South Coast Peru, A.D. 200 - 400. Terra cotta. Height 7¼ in. Buckingham Fund 55.2100.

Ex Coll. Gaffron. Reference: Kubler, G., p. 145, fig. A.

12 *Puma Stirrup Spout Vessel.* Nazca Culture, South Coast Peru, A.D. 1 - 200. Terra cotta. Height 8¼ in. Buckingham Fund 55.1848.

The incised decoration, a Paracas holdover, identifies this piece as having been made at the beginning of the Nazca period. Ex Coll. Gaffron. References: AIC Quarterly, Vol. 50, No. 1, p. 3, ill.; Chicago, Art Institute 1957b, p. 41, ill.

13 *Trophy-Head Jar.* Nazca Culture, South Coast Peru, A.D. 400 - 700. Terra cotta. Height 6 in. Gift of Mr. and Mrs. Nathan Cummings 57.425.

Trophy heads were taken by the Nazca; in this example, the killing wound appears in the middle of the forehead. Ex Coll. Wassermann. References: Encyclopedia of World Art, color plate 190; Sawyer, A. 1954, p. 29, ill.; Wassermann, B., pl. 549.

14 *Portrait Head Jar*. Mochica Culture, North Coast Peru, A.D. 300 - 500. Terra cotta. Height 8⅝ in. Buckingham Fund 55.2349.

Ex Coll. Gaffron. References: AIC Quarterly Vol. 46, No. 2, cover ill.; Berlin, Staatlichen Museum, taf. XIV; Doering, H. U. 1952, figs. 220, 221; Keleman, P., pl. 106b; Kutscher, G. 1950, pl. 6; Lehmann, W. and Doering, H. U., fig. 80; Leicht, H., pl. 14, lower right.

15 *Warrior Jar*. Mochica Culture, North Coast Peru, A.D. 400 - 600. Terra cotta. Height 19½ in. Buckingham Fund 55.2356b.

Ex Coll. Gaffron. References: AIC Quarterly, Vol. 46, No. 2, p. 28, ill.

16 *Handle Spout Vessel*. Mochica Culture, North Coast Peru, A.D. 400 - 600. Terra cotta. Height 10⅝ in. Buckingham Fund 55.2291.

A frieze of running messengers is painted on the body of the vessel. Ex Coll. Gaffron. References: Christensen, E., fig. 235; Doering, H. U. 1952, fig. 184.

17 *Portrait Stirrup Spout Vessel*. Mochica Culture, North Coast Peru, A.D. 400 - 600. Terra cotta. Height 14 in. Buckingham Fund 55.2338.

A superb and unusually large example of the Mochica portrait style. Ex Coll. Gaffron. References: AIC Annual Report 1957, cover ill.; Bird, J., p. 197, fig. 46; Christensen, E., pl. 233; Doering, H. U. 1936, cover ill. and p. 601; Doering, H. U. 1952, fig. 222; Lehmann, W. and Doering, H. U., fig. 81; Leicht, H., fig. 3.

15

16

17

18

19

PERU/MOCHICA

20

21

18 *Marsh Scene Stirrup Spout Vessel*. Mochica Culture, North Coast Peru, A.D. 400 - 600. Terra cotta. Height 9⅞ in. Buckingham Fund 55.2251.

Ex Coll. Gaffron. References: Doering, H. U. 1952, fig. 178; Kutscher, G. 1950, fig. 8, p. 11 (drawing); Lehmann, W. and Doering, H. U., fig. 37.

19 *Bean Warrior Stirrup Spout Vessel*. Mochica Culture, North Coast Peru, A.D. 500 - 800. Terra cotta. Height 10¼ in. Buckingham Fund 55.2274.

A masterpiece of Mochican vase painting in which the motif of the bean has been carried from the decoration on the spout to the shape of the warriors themselves. Ex Coll. Gaffron. References: AIC Quarterly, Vol. XLVI, No. 2, p. 29,

ill.; Bennett, W., fig. 40; Chicago, Arts Club, No. 84, ill.; Christensen, E., pl. 236; Minneapolis Institute of Art, p. 37.

20 *Puma and Warrior Stirrup Spout Vessel*. Mochica Culture, North Coast Peru, A.D. 400 - 600. Terra cotta. Height 12 in. Buckingham Fund 55.2264.

Ex Coll. Gaffron. References: Bennett, W., fig. 41; Kutscher, G. 1950, fig. 30, p. 28 (drawing); Lehmann, W. and Doering, H. U., fig. 85.

21 *Stirrup Spout Vessel*. Mochica Culture, North Coast Peru, A.D. 400 - 600. Terra cotta. Height 11⅞ in. Gift of Mr. and Mrs. Nathan Cummings 58.610.

A fish demon holding a knife is here represented. Ex Coll. Wassermann. Reference: Wassermann, B., No. 109, pl. 37.

22

23

24

25

22 *Lintel*. North Central Coast Peru, A.D. 1300 - 1500. Wood. Length, 54 in. Buckingham Fund 55.2470.
Ex Coll. Gaffron.

23 *Alpaca Ceremonial Container*. Inca Culture, Peru, A.D. 1438 - 1532. Black limestone (?). Height 2⅞ in. Buckingham Fund 55.2509.
Ex Coll. Gaffron. Reference: Chicago, Art Institute 1957b, p. 46, ill.

24 *Incised Rattle Head*. Nazca Culture, South Coast Peru, A.D. 1 - 200. Gourd. Height 5¼ in. Buckingham Fund 55.2499.
This piece was found at Hacienda Tunga, Nazca Valley, about 1910, when it was purchased by Eduard Gaffron. Ex Coll. Gaffron. Reference: Los Angeles County Museum, No. 228, ill. p. 76.

25 *Blackware Double Vessel*. Inca Culture, Chimu workmanship, A.D. 1300 - 1500. Terra cotta. Height 7¼ in. Buckingham Fund 55.2403.
Ex Coll. Gaffron.

26 *Tapestry Weave Fragment.* Mochica Culture (?), North Coast Peru (?), A.D. 500 - 1000 (?). Cotton and wool. Height (area shown) 11 in., width 10⅝. Buckingham Fund 55.1653.

Although traditionally given to the Mochica, the design is closely related to Tiahuanaco weavings of the South and Central Coast. If this piece is a Mochican product, its state of preservation is extraordinary. Ex Coll. Gaffron. Reference: Lehmann, W. and Doering, H. U., pl. 119, top.

26

27

28

29

30

Interlocking Tapestry Panel. Post-Tiahuanaco Style, Central Coast Peru, A.D. 1000 - 1500. Cotton. Height 13¼ in., width 13¼. Buckingham Fund 55.1762.

A large human figure is surrounded by anthropomorphic designs. Ex Coll. Gaffron. Reference: Lehmann, W. and Doering, H. U., color plate VIII, bottom.

Slit Tapestry Fragment. Pachacamac (?), Central Coast Peru, after A.D. 1000. Cotton and wool. Height (area shown) 15¾ in., width 16¼. Buckingham Fund 55.1684.

A three-dimensional effect has been given to the animal pelt representation through the creation of an uncut velvet weave. Ex Coll. Gaffron. Reference: Doering, H. U. 1952, pl. 68.

Slit Tapestry Fragment. Post-Tiahuanaco Style, Central Coast Peru. A.D. 1000 - 1300. Cotton and wool. Height (area shown) 9⅛ in., width 8¼. Buckingham Fund 55.1706.

Shown here are warriors with large white birds. Ex Coll. Gaffron. References: Lehmann, W. and Doering, H. U., color plate X; AIC Quarterly, Vol. 46, No. 2, p. 29, ill.

Interlocking Tapestry Poncho. Coast Tiahuanaco Culture, South Coast Peru, A.D. 800 - 1100. Cotton and wool. Height (area shown) 8⅝ in., width 22½. Buckingham Fund 55.1784.

The feline motif, here abstracted to its most basic elements, is common to Tiahuanaco weaving designs. Ex Coll. Gaffron. References: Bennett, W., figs. 6, 91; Christensen, E., fig. 252; Doering, H. U. 1952, pl. 101; Lehmann, W. and Doering, H. U., color plate III; Minneapolis Institute of Art, fig. 7; Lothrop, S. K., p. 214, ill.

Slit Tapestry Fragment. Central Coast Peru, A.D. 1000 - 1500. Cotton and wool. Height (area shown) 17½ in., width 19. Buckingham Fund 55.1680.

Monkey warriors are shown in battle. Ex Coll. Gaffron.

Shield. Coast Tiahuanaco Culture, South Coast Peru, A.D. 800 - 1000. Split bamboo, cotton, animal hide, red and white pigment. Diameter 15⅝ in. Buckingham Fund 55.2506.

This remarkably well preserved and perhaps unique shield shows the motif of a puma warrior surrounded by winged figures. Ex Coll. Gaffron.

Slit Tapestry Panel. Nazca Culture, South Coast Peru, A.D. 200 - 700. Cotton and wool. Height 9¾ in., width 19¾. Buckingham Fund 55.1748.

Ex Coll. Gaffron.

Interlocking Tapestry Fragment. Nazca Culture, South Coast Peru, A.D. 200 - 600. Cotton. Height 15¾ in., width (area shown) 35¾. Mrs. Edwin A. Seipp Restricted Fund 56.79.

The central motif consists of a large feline figure.

32

33

34

35

MEXICO/TEOTIHUACAN, CLASSIC VERACRUZ

35 *Funerary Mask*. Teotihuacan Culture, Mexico, A.D. 500 - 800. Stone. Height 7½ in. Wirt D. Walker Fund and Primitive Art Purchase Fund 63.260.

It is now believed that such masks were made to be buried with notables. None has ever been scientifically excavated. Reference: AIC Quarterly, Vol. 57, No. 4, ill.

36 *Hacha*. Classic Veracruz Style, Veracruz, A.D. 600 - 1000. Limestone. Height 13¼ in. Primitive Art Purchase Fund 62.701.

It is believed that these objects were part of an elaborate costume worn on a broad belt during ceremonial ball games. The extensive use of the scroll form probably indicates a Late Classic date. Reference: AIC Annual Report 1962 - 1963, p. 27, ill.

36

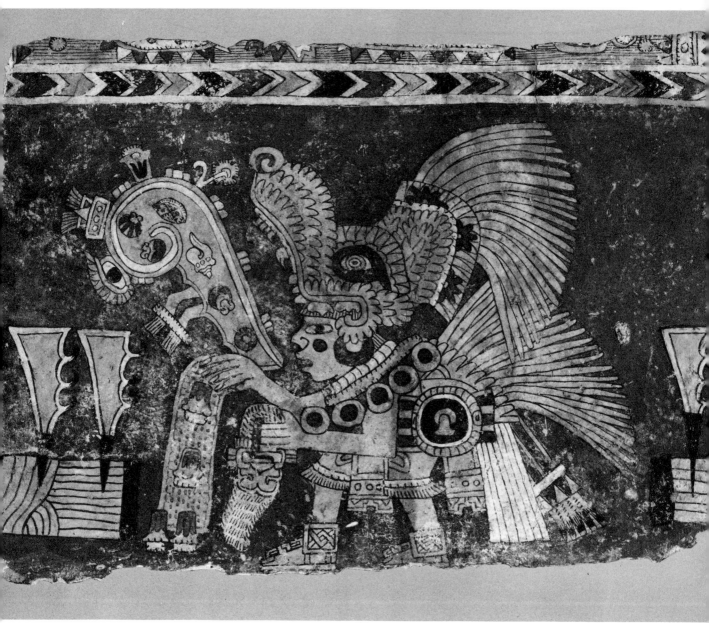

37

MEXICO/TEOTIHUACAN, COLIMA

38

39

37 *Rain Priest Fresco.* Teotihuacan Culture, A.D. 400 - 800. Adobe, lime, red pigment. Length 36⅝ in. Primitive Art Purchase Fund 62.702.

A rain priest is seen bringing water and seeds to a field of maguey. Water symbols in the form of flowers, shells, and other shapes can be seen falling from the priest's right hand and in the speech glyph. Other frescoes from this same building are known, one of which is in the Cleveland Museum of Art (62.252).

38 *Urn Fragments.* Teotihuacan Culture. A.D. 500 - 900. Terra cotta, traces of yellow, red and green pigment. Height 14½ in. Gift of Joseph P. Antonow 62.1073.

This elaborate sculpture is reconstructed. It once decorated a large urn or brazier; either a fire god or an old man is represented. Reference: AIC Annual Report 1962 - 1963, p. 29, ill.

39 *Humpbacked Figure.* Colima Culture, West Coast Mexico, A.D. 500 - 900. Terra cotta. Height 11⅛ in. Gift of Joseph P. Antonow 61.894. Ex Coll. Michel.

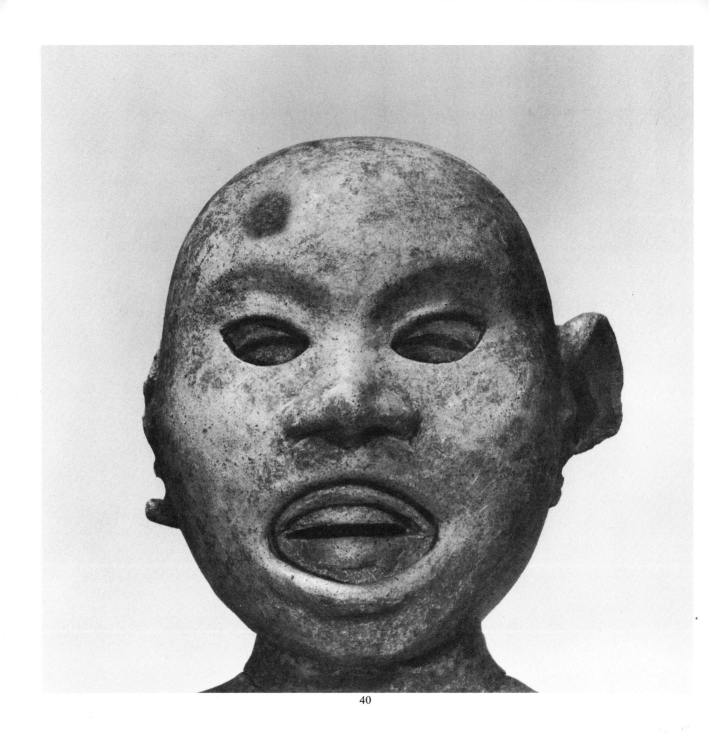

40

MEXICO/VERACRUZ, COLIMA

41

42

40 *Figure of Xipe.* Aztec Culture (?), Central Veracruz, ca. A.D. 1400 - 1550. Terra cotta, traces of red pigment. Height 23¼ in. Gift of Mr. and Mrs. Samuel A. Marx 60.905.

Although originally thought to have been from the Remojadas area, and made during the classic period, this figure is now believed to be of the later Aztec period. A priest is shown wearing the skin of a sacrificial victim. References: AIC Quarterly, Vol. 54, No. 3, p. 6, ill.; Chicago, Art Institute 1960, No. 28, ill.

41 *Pair of Figures.* Late Archaic Colima Culture, West Coast Mexico, A.D. 100 - 400. Terra cotta. Height 10¾ in. and 15¾ in. Gift of Mr. and Mrs. James W. Alsdorf 62.1070-71. Reference: AIC Quarterly, Vol. 57, No. 1, p. 9, ill.

42 *Pair of Dancing Warriors.* Archaic Colima Culture, West Coast Mexico, ca. 100 B.C. Terra cotta. Height 8 in. and 8¼ in. Primitive Art Purchase Fund 57.249a-b.

Although probably made for burial, both figures contain small whistles, which perhaps indicates an unknown ceremonial function. Reference: AIC Quarterly, Vol. 57, No. 1, p. 8, ill.

44

45

46

43 *Standing Warrior*. Maya Culture, Jaina Style, Mexico, A.D. 400 - 800. Terra cotta, traces of blue and orange pigment. Height 12¼ in. Primitive Art Purchase Fund and Edward E. Ayer Fund 63.272.

The famous clay figurines in the Jaina style are among the most exquisite small sculptures from ancient Mexico. This particular example shows a warrior wearing a jaguar mask on his forehead. The right forearm, right foot, and part of the shield are restored.

44 *Jaguar Throne*. Manabi Culture, Ecuador, ca. A.D. 1000. Stone. Height 17¼ in. Gift of Mr. and Mrs. Raymond Wielgus 58.303.

Many of these thrones, which were used ceremonially, have been found in house ruins and the remains of religious enclosures. References: AIC Quarterly, Vol. 51, No. 4, p. 87, fig. 4; Chicago, Art Institute 1957b, pp. 22, 23, ill.

45 *Pedestal Bowl*. Coclé Culture, Sitio Conte, Panama, A.D. 1000 - 1300. Terra cotta. Diameter 10¼ in. Mrs. Chauncey B. Borland Fund 61.2.

Ex Coll. Dade.

46 *Tripod Bowl*. Region of Los Tuxtlas, Southern Veracruz, Mexico, A.D. 400 - 800. Terra cotta. Diameter 13⅜ in. Buckingham Fund. 61.914.

A similar bowl is on loan to the collections of the American Museum of Natural History (T109-156).

47

48

47 *Plaque Fragment*. Benin Culture, Nigeria, 17th century (?). Bronze. Height 13¾ in. Samuel P. Avery Fund 33.782.

This fragment depicting a warrior is part of a larger plaque that once decorated the walls of Benin City. Reference: AIC Bulletin, Vol. 28, No. 1, pp. 19-20, ill.

√ 48 *Female Figure*. Dogon Tribe, Mali Federation. Wood with patina. Height 25½ in. Samuel P. Avery Fund 58.290.

Such figures are usually associated with the highly important ancestor cult developed by the Dogon.

√ 49 *Mask*. Dogon Tribe, Mali Federation. Wood, white pigment, cowrie shells, fiber. Height 33¼ in. Simeon P. Williams Fund and Samuel P. Avery Fund 58.291.

This type of mask was used in dances to honor a mythical bird. Reference: Long, C. H., pl. 21.

AFRICA/BENIN, DOGON

49

50

AFRICA/BAGA

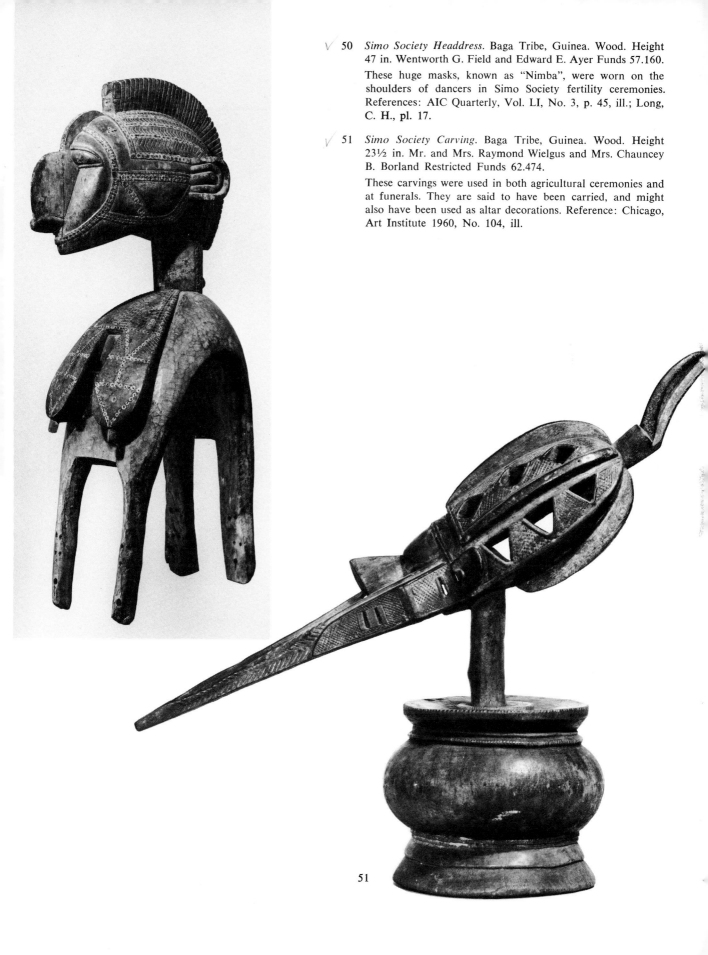

50 *Simo Society Headdress*. Baga Tribe, Guinea. Wood. Height 47 in. Wentworth G. Field and Edward E. Ayer Funds 57.160.

These huge masks, known as "Nimba", were worn on the shoulders of dancers in Simo Society fertility ceremonies. References: AIC Quarterly, Vol. LI, No. 3, p. 45, ill.; Long, C. H., pl. 17.

51 *Simo Society Carving*. Baga Tribe, Guinea. Wood. Height 23½ in. Mr. and Mrs. Raymond Wielgus and Mrs. Chauncey B. Borland Restricted Funds 62.474.

These carvings were used in both agricultural ceremonies and at funerals. They are said to have been carried, and might also have been used as altar decorations. Reference: Chicago, Art Institute 1960, No. 104, ill.

51

52

53

52 *Male Fetish Figure*. Basongye Tribe, Republic of Congo (Leopoldville). Wood, brass tacks, animal horn, brass. Height 28⅛ in. Mr. and Mrs. Nathan Cummings Restricted Fund **61.912.**

Large fetish figures were thought to have the power to protect their owners from disease, enemy attack, and other such dangers. The additions of other substances to the wood sculpture added to its magical power.

54

55

53 *Male Fetish Figure*. Bakongo Tribe, Republic of Congo (Leopoldville). Wood, mirrors. Height 12¼ in. Gift of Mr. and Mrs. Herbert Baker 61.1176.

Reference: Lake Forest, Illinois, College, figs. 17, 17a.

54 *Reliquary Head*. Fang Tribe, Gabon. Wood. Height 10½ in. Gift of Mr. and Mrs. Raymond Wielgus 58.301.

This piece was stolen from the Art Institute collection in 1961. References: Chicago, Art Institute 1957a, No. 30; Iowa State University School of Fine Arts, No. 30, cover ill.; Milwaukee, Layton School of Art, No. 32; Toledo Museum of Art, No. 106, ill. See also note for the following No. 55.

55 *Male Reliquary Figure*. Fang Tribe, Gabon. Wood. Height 18 in. Gift of Mr. and Mrs. Raymond Wielgus 58.302.

The Fang placed such figures over boxes containing the remains of the family dead to protect them from evil spirits. References: Chicago, Art Institute 1957a, No. 31; Milwaukee, Layton School of Art, No. 33; Segy, L., figs. 80, 81.

56

AFRICA/BAMBARA

57

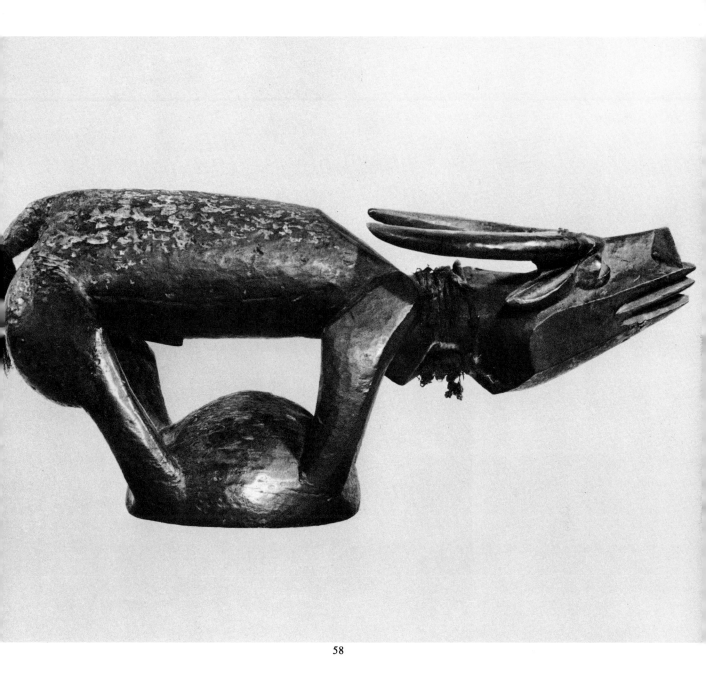

58

Kono Society Fetish. Bambara Tribe, Mali Federation. Wood, cloth, heavy sacrificial patina. Height 17¼ in. Gift of Mr. and Mrs. Harold X. Weinstein 61.1177.

These fetishes, known as "Boli", were used as altars by the Bambara. They represented a microcosm of all that was important to their universe. The magic power of the figures is continually renewed through the addition of sacrificial materials, which accounts for the thick patina of the sculpture.

References: AIC Quarterly, Vol. 52, No. 1, p. 2, ill.; Long, C. H., pl. 3.

57   *Kono Society Mask.* Bambara Tribe, Mali Federation. Wood, animal horns, string, animal hair and sacrificial patina. Length 32½ in. Gift of Allan Frumkin 62.106.

Reference: AIC Quarterly, Vol. 52, No. 1, p. 5, ill.

58   *Water Buffalo.* Bambara Tribe, Mali Federation. Wood, string, hair, metal staples. Height 14¼ in. Mr. and Mrs. Samuel A. Marx Restricted Fund and Wirt D. Walker Fund 61.557.

The use of this sculpture is unknown, but since the dome on which the feet rest is hollow, it may have been worn as an elaborate headdress. References: AIC Quarterly, Vol. 52, No. 1, p. 2, ill.; Denver Art Museum, p. 14, ill.

59

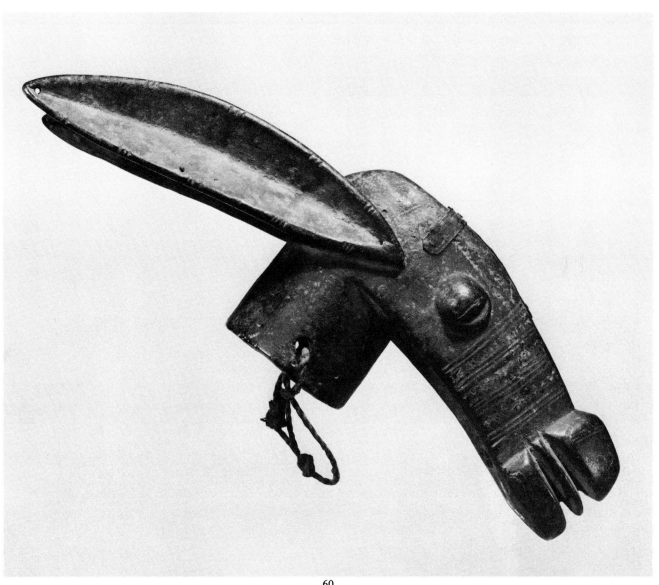

60

62

63

64

61 *Mask*. Guro Tribe, Ivory Coast. Wood, monkey fur, white pigment. Height 14 in. Buckingham Fund 58.118.

A similar mask in this rare style is in the Paris collection of Christophe Tzara. Reference: Toledo Museum of Art, No. 47, ill.

62 *Ekpo Society Mask*. Bini Tribe, Nigeria. Wood, traces of white pigment. Height 14⅞ in. Mr. and Mrs. James W. Alsdorf Restricted Fund 61.913.

Reference: AIC Annual Report 1961 - 1962, p. 18, ill. See also note for No. 73.

63 *Mask*. Mayumbe Tribe (?), Republic of Congo (Leopold-ville). Wood, white and black pigment. Height 7¾ in. Mr. and Mrs. James W. Alsdorf Restricted Fund 62.700.

Little is known of the use of these masks; they are thought to represent spirits of the dead.

64 *Mask*. Attie Tribe, District of Grand Lahou, Ivory Coast. Wood, monkey fur. Height 10⅜ in. Primitive Art Purchase Fund 62.473.

Ex Coll. Bediat.

65

66

67

68

65 *Helmet Mask*. Senufo Tribe, Korhogo District, Ivory Coast. Wood. Length 40⅛ in. Primitive Art Purchase Fund 63.842.

Known popularly as firespitter masks, these helmets were used in rituals to drive away soul-eaters. The inclusion of many different animal forms is indicative of a complex iconography.

66 *Gelede Society Mask*. Yoruba Tribe, Nigeria. Wood. Height 13¼ in. Winter and Hirsch Purchase Fund 63.843.

This mask was used in plays given by the Gelede cult, a men's increase society.

67 *Animal Mask*. Dan Tribe, Liberia. Wood. Height 7¼ in. Primitive Art Purchase Fund 63.273.

68 *Mask*. Bobo Diulasso Tribe, Mali Federation. Wood, red, white and black pigment, fibers. Height 45 in. Mrs. Chauncey B. Borland Restricted Fund 58.116.

The Bobo used such masks in agricultural ceremonies. Reference: Long, C. H., pl. 18.

69 *Ghost Mask.* M'Pongwe Tribe (?), Ogowe River, Gabon. Wood, raffia, white pigment. Height 10¼ in. (mask only). Primitive Art Purchase Fund 64.230.

The mask was worn in funerary rites. A female spirit is here represented.

70 *Fertility Doll.* Ashanti Tribe, Ghana. Wood, string, beads. Height 10⅜ in. Gift of Mr. and Mrs. Herbert Baker 63.850.

Such dolls are worn by Ashanti women to ensure fertility, and to protect the well-being of their children.

71 *Ancestor Figure.* Baule Tribe, Ivory Coast. Wood, brass tacks. Height 22½ in. Edward E. Ayer Fund 60.802.

Ex Colls. Derain, Wielgus. References: Chicago, Art Institute 1957a, No. 23; Milwaukee, Layton School of Art, No. 26.

72 *Mask.* Bapende Tribe, Republic of Congo (Leopoldville). Wood, raffia, traces of red pigment. Height 10¾ in. Mr. and Mrs. Nathan Cummings Restricted Fund 64.228.

Bapende masks are worn at ceremonies for young initiates who have finished their schooling and are ready to enter the adult life of the tribe.

70

71

72

73 *Four Ekpo Society Masks.* Ibibio Tribe, Nigeria. Wood,
paint, raffia, feathers, nails. Maximum height 12⅜ in. Gift
of Mr. and Mrs. Raymond Wielgus 63.384-387.

These masks were used in Ekpo Society ceremonies which
were concerned with ancestor worship and with maintaining
order within the Society.

House Post. Maori Tribe, New Zealand. Late 18th century(?). Wood. Height 53 in. Ada Turnbull Hertle Fund 58.404.

Reference: Long, C.H., pl. 5.

Neckrest. Sepik River Course, New Guinea. Wood, bamboo, shell, rattan, traces of polychrome. Length 16⅝ in. Anonymous gift 57.623.

Sepik neckrests rarely display the complexity of carving found on this particular example.

House Mask. Sepik River Course, New Guinea. Cork, shell, rattan, red and white pigment. Height 16 in. Buckingham Fund 58.119.

Such masks were made to decorate the gables of men's ceremonial clubhouses.

75

74

76

77

78

77 *Skull Mask*. New Britain. Anterior portion of human skull, wood, rattan, human hair, parinarium nut paste, red pigment. Height 10¼ in. Gift of Allan Frumkin 60.904.

78 *Mask*. Ambrym Island, New Hebrides. Hemp fibers, bark, traces of color. Height 29 in. Gift of Allan Frumkin 58.300. Such masks were used for grade society functions. They may represent ancestral spirits.

79 *Ceremonial Board*. Elema Tribe, Papuan Gulf, New Guinea. Wood, red, white and black pigment. Height 60 in. Gift of Mrs. Gilbert Chapman 51.421.
Reference: Newton, D., fig. 243.

80 *Sea Spirit Mask*. New Caledonia. Wood. Height 18⅛ in. Gift of Mr. and Mrs. Raymond Wielgus 62.1083.

79   80

Select Bibliography

AIC see Chicago, Art Institute

Bennett, Wendell
1954   Ancient Arts of the Andes. New York

Berlin, Staatlichen Museum
1931   Altamerikanische Kunst, December

Bird, Junius
1962   Art and Life in Old Peru
In Curator, Vol. V, No. 2, American Museum of
   Natural History

Burlington Magazine
1964   Volume CVI, No. 170, November 1964

Chicago, Art Institute
AIC Annual Reports, Bulletins and Quarterlies
   as specifically listed in references
1957a African Art in the Collection of
   Mr. and Mrs. Raymond Wielgus
1957b Animal Sculpture in Pre-Columbian Art
1960   Primitive Art in Chicago Collections

Chicago, Arts Club
1962   Wit and Humor in Art

Christensen, Erwin O.
1955   Primitive Art. New York

Denver Art Museum
1964   Art of Africa. Quarterly, Spring

Dockstader, Frederick D.
Indian Art of the Americas Before and After Columbus
In Art in America, Vol. 49 no. 3, 1961, p. 24-43

Doering, Heinrich U.
1936   Porträts der Vorzeit
1952   The Art of Ancient Peru. New York

Encyclopedia of World Art
1957   Vol. I. New York

Iowa State University, School of Fine Arts
1956   African Sculpture

Keleman, Pal
1943   Medieval American Art, 2 vols. New York

Kubler, George
1962   The Art and Architecture of Ancient
   America. Baltimore

Kutscher, Gerdt
1950   Chimu, eine Altindische Hochkultur. Berlin

Lake Forest, Illinois, College
1962   African Art. Herbert Baker Collection

Lehmann, Walter and Doering, Heinrich U.
1924   Kunstgeschichte des Alten Peru. Berlin

Leicht, Hermann
1960   Pre Inca Art and Culture. New York

Long, Charles H.
1963   Alpha, The Myths of Creation. New York

Los Angeles County Museum
1964   Gold Before Columbus

Lothrop, Samuel K.
1964   Treasures of Ancient America. Geneva

Milwaukee, Layton School of Art
1957   African Sculpture

Minneapolis Institute of Art
1954   Bulletin, Vol. XLIII, No. 5, May

Newton, Douglas
1961   Art Styles of the Papuan Gulf.
   The Museum of Primitive Art. New York

New York, Cooper Union
1951   Alter Ego. Masks: Their Art and Use

Sawyer, Alan R.
1954   The Nathan Cummings Collection of Ancient
   Peruvian Art. Chicago
1961   Paracas and Nazca Iconography
   in Essays in Pre-Columbian Art and Archaeology.
   Cambridge, U.S.A.

Segy, Ladislaus
1952   African Sculpture Speaks. New York

Toledo Museum of Art
1958   The African Image

Wassermann, B. J.
1938   Ceramicas del Antiguo Peru. Buenos Aires

Zahan, D.
1960   Sociétés d'Initiation Bambara. Paris